How to Daz.

Twelfth Night

Irene Yates

Brilliant Publications

Introduction

The aim of this book is to lead students to a deeper understanding of the play through a variety of exercises which will at once stimulate, amuse and challenge.

There are quiz words, Shakespeare's words, no words (where they are missing from the cloze passages), alternative words and other words to stimulate discussion about the play, in either pairs or larger groups.

The book is intended primarily for teachers of Shakespeare at both KS3 and KS4. They will find that the activities provide stimulus for assignments for students of all abilities. There is a choice of self-contained activities which cross the ability range but which are suitable in particular for lower ability groups.

It is suggested that teachers first go through the play with the 'scene-by-scene' summary and the original text. They can then pick exercises appropriate for their groups, with possibly the easier, more 'fun' types first, and the more challenging ones after, as students become more familiar with the play.

Some exercises are ideal as homework tasks. Others are useful as a starting point for group work, both oral and written. All the sheets are easy to administer and mark. Answers to some of the exercises are given on pages 48 and 49.

These worksheets can also be helpful when teaching the drama units of the 'Certificate of Achievement' courses in English for the less able students in KS4.

• •

Publisher's information

Published by Brilliant Publications
1 Church View
Sparrow Hall Farm
Edlesborough
Dunstable
Bedfordshire LU6 2ES

Tel: 01525 229720
Fax: 01525 229725
Website: www.brilliantpublications.co.uk
E-mail: sales@brilliantpublications.co.uk

Written by Irene Yates
Illustrated by Ray and Corrine Burrows
Front cover by Ray and Corrine Burrows
Printed in the UK by Alden Group Limited
© Irene Yates

ISBN   1 903853 34 6

First published 2003
10 9 8 7 6 5 4 3 2 1

Contents

Please note that while all Act and Scene numbers are the same in every edition, the line numbers will vary. You may need to look several lines before or after to find the exact place. The teacher is advised to check and amend the numbers before photocopying.

Twelfth Night

The main story or plot

Orsino, the Duke of Illyria, is in love with the Countess Olivia. She doesn't want to know. She is sad because her brother has died.

Viola and Sebastian are twins. They are shipwrecked in a storm. Viola thinks Sebastian is dead. He thinks she is dead.

Viola disguises herself as a boy and gets a job as a servant to Orsino. She calls herself Cesario. Orsino gives 'him' a job. Everyone thinks that Cesario is really a boy; nobody suspects that he is actually a girl in disguise. Orsino sends Cesario to tell Olivia how much he loves her. Olivia falls for Cesario. Meanwhile, Cesario, who is really Viola, has fallen for Orsino.

The subplot (secondary story)

Olivia has an uncle, Sir Toby Belch, who likes to have a good time. He is very cunning. His friend, Sir Andrew Aguecheek, is very rich and Sir Toby keeps taking money from him and telling him that Olivia might marry him. Olivia's head servant, Malvolio, doesn't like the two men and tells them off for being noisy and drunk.

Olivia's lady-in-waiting, Maria, decides to get her own back on Malvolio. She fakes a love letter to him from Olivia. Malvolio goes to Olivia, dressed in silly clothes and acting in a silly way. This is what the letter tells him to do. Olivia thinks he's gone mad. She hands him over to Sir Toby, who locks him up.

More confusion

Meanwhile, Sebastian, Viola's twin brother, has been rescued by a sea-captain called Antonio. Sebastian decides to go to Orsino's court. Antonio follows him in secret. He has to keep in hiding because in the past he had been involved in a sea battle against Orsino. He leaves Sebastian to explore the city alone and lends him his money.

All this time Cesario is still coming to see Olivia. Sir Andrew thinks there's something going on between them. Sir Toby forces him to challenge Cesario to a duel. Antonio turns up. He thinks Cesario is Sebastian and rescues him. But then he is arrested himself for piracy. He asks Cesario for his money back, thinking he is Sebastian. But Cesario says he doesn't know what he's talking about. Antonio thinks Sebastian has lied and cheated him. Cesario (Viola) guesses that Sebastian is alive.

Things get worse …

There is a commotion in which Sebastian gives Sir Andrew a beating, with Sir Toby joining in. Olivia meets Sebastian and thinks he is Cesario. She talks him into going home with her and they get engaged.

Orsino arrives at Olivia's house, with Cesario. Antonio is dragged in by the police and Cesario recognizes him as the person who rescued him from the duel with Sir Andrew. Antonio complains that Cesario has betrayed him. Olivia turns up and says that she is betrothed to Cesario. Orsino is furious. Then Sir Toby and Sir Andrew appear, saying that Cesario has beaten them up.

Happy ending?

Finally, Sebastian comes in and everyone understands what's been happening. When Orsino learns that Cesario is actually Viola, he realizes he's in love with her. Malvolio arrives and asks Olivia why she's been treating him so badly. He shows her the letter but she tells him she didn't write it. Malvolio realizes he's been made a fool of and storms off, promising revenge.

The story goes...
a scene-by-scene account of the play

The setting
The action takes place in Illyria. It is a friendly, dreamlike, faraway land. It is a fantasy world. It is a land of the imagination, a bit like an enchanted forest.

Act 1 Scene 1
Orsino is the Duke of Illyria. He is madly in love with Olivia. Olivia is sad because her brother is dead. She doesn't want to speak to anyone for seven years.

Act 1 Scene 2
A ship is wrecked in a storm. The Captain, his sailors and Viola survive. Viola's twin brother, Sebastian, may have drowned. The Captain tells Viola about the Duke Orsino and Olivia. Viola decides to disguise herself as a boy and become a servant to Orsino.

Act 1 Scene 3
In Olivia's house, her uncle, Sir Toby Belch, has made her cross. He wants her to get on with her life. He drinks a lot with his friend, Sir Andrew Aguecheek, who is a rich good-for-nothing. Sir Andrew wants to leave but Sir Toby talks him out of it.

Act 1 Scene 4
Viola calls herself Cesario. Orsino likes 'the boy' at once. He wants him to go to Olivia and tell her how much he loves her. Cesario agrees to do his best, but the real truth is that he, as Viola, has fallen in love with Orsino.

Act 1 Scene 5
There is a lot of clowning about with Feste, the fool, and Malvolio, Olivia's head servant. Cesario comes to tell Olivia that the Duke loves her. Olivia falls in love with Cesario. She doesn't know that Cesario is really a girl. Olivia gives Malvolio a ring to take to Cesario, pretending that it is the one 'he' had left behind.

Act 2 Scene 1

Sebastian is alive. He was rescued by Antonio, a seafaring captain. Sebastian thinks his sister is dead. Sebastian decides to go to Duke Orsino's court. Antonio decides to follow him.

Act 2 Scene 2

Malvolio catches up with Cesario and tries to give him the ring. Cesario refuses to take it. Malvolio throws it on the ground and goes away. Cesario realizes that Olivia has fallen for him and doesn't know what to do, because, of course, 'he' is really Viola, a woman.

Act 2 Scene 3

Sir Toby and Sir Andrew are joking around, getting drunk. Feste comes in and they ask him to sing, for which they pay him. Feste sings, then they all sing together. Maria warns them to keep the noise down or Olivia will get Malvolio to throw them out. Malvolio storms in. He and Sir Toby have a row and Malvolio goes off in a huff. Maria plots with Sir Toby and Sir Andrew to make a fool of Malvolio by sending him a letter, pretending it's from Olivia. Maria goes and the two men stay up, getting more drunk.

Act 2 Scene 4

Orsino wants Feste to come and sing a love song. He asks Cesario about love and who he is in love with. Cesario (Viola) describes a woman who is very like the Duke. Feste breaks the tension by singing the song. Orsino begs Cesario to go to Olivia again. Cesario tries to tell Orsino that Olivia doesn't love him but he doesn't believe it. Orsino says that men feel more deeply than women but Cesario tells him that women can feel as much. She pretends she has a sister and describes how she loves but she is really talking about her own feelings for the Duke.

Act 2 Scene 5

Sir Toby, Sir Andrew and Fabian (one of Olivia's servants) hide in a hedge. Maria drops the letter for Malvolio to pick up. He already thinks Olivia finds him handsome. He reads the letter and thinks it's about him. It tells him to do silly things to prove he loves Olivia. He decides to go along with it. Sir Toby and Fabian think it's really funny. Maria tells them to watch how Malvolio behaves when he sees Olivia.

Act 3 Scene 1

Feste makes lots of clever jokes to Cesario. Cesario is very impressed with the fool's wit. Sir Toby and Sir Andrew arrive. Sir Andrew is worried that Olivia seems to like Cesario.

Cesario tries to tell Olivia how much Orsino loves her but Olivia tells Cesario it is him she likes. Cesario tries to put Olivia off, but it only makes her more interested.

Act 3 Scene 2

Sir Andrew is really upset at seeing Olivia and Cesario together. Fabian tells him Olivia is just trying to make him jealous. Sir Toby suggests that Sir Andrew could impress Olivia by challenging Cesario to a duel. Sir Toby and Fabian think this is very funny.

Maria tells them to watch Malvolio, who is behaving ridiculously – wearing yellow stockings and constantly grinning.

Act 3 Scene 3

Away from the court, Sebastian is in town. Antonio has followed him to make sure he's okay. Sebastian wants to go exploring but this isn't a good idea for Antonio, as he might be recognized and arrested for a battle he once had some time ago with one of Orsino's ships. Antonio gives Sebastian his money and arranges to meet him later.

Act 3 Scene 4

While Olivia is waiting for Cesario, she sends for Malvolio. Maria tells her that he is acting like a real idiot. Malvolio comes in and tries to charm Olivia. He mentions a line from her letter. Olivia is really confused and thinks he's gone mad. She tells Sir Toby to take charge of Malvolio and goes to meet Cesario.

Sir Toby, Fabian and Maria all laugh at Malvolio and talk to him as if he's mad. The letter told him to be rude to them, so he is. They decide to lock him up, to make the joke even funnier.

Sir Andrew has written his challenge to Cesario, but Sir Toby thinks that what Sir Andrew has written is terrible and decides not to give it to Cesario.

Olivia gives Cesario a picture of herself but Cesario tells her it would be better to give her love to Orsino.

Sir Toby tries to frighten Cesario, telling him how brave and fierce Sir Andrew is. Cesario makes excuses because 'he' doesn't want to fight. After Sir Toby leaves, Fabian keeps winding up Cesario.

Sir Toby tells Sir Andrew not to be afraid. He also tells him Cesario is a great fighter. Cesario is almost ready to admit he is really Viola.

Antonio comes rushing in, thinking Cesario is Sebastian. He threatens Sir Andrew. The police, who have recognized Antonio, turn up to arrest him. Antonio asks Cesario for his money, still thinking he is Sebastian. Cesario doesn't understand. Antonio thinks Sebastian has betrayed him. He's taken away.

Viola realizes Antonio thinks she's Sebastian and works out that her twin brother must be alive somewhere.

Sir Toby thinks Cesario is a coward and that even Sir Andrew could beat him, and they all follow after Viola.

Act 4 Scene 1

Feste has come to fetch Cesario. He meets Sebastian instead and thinks he's Cesario. Sebastian refuses to go with him. He gives Feste some money to leave him alone.

Sir Andrew – thinking Sebastian is Cesario and therefore a coward – takes a swipe at him with his sword. Sebastian hits Sir Andrew and knocks him backwards and pulls out his dagger.

Sir Toby grabs Sebastian's arm. Feste goes off to get Olivia. Sebastian pulls himself free and he and Sir Toby draw their swords.

Olivia arrives in the nick of time. She's angry with Sir Toby for fighting the person she thinks is Cesario. She sends Sir Toby away and invites Sebastian into the house, still thinking he is Cesario. Sebastian is confused but goes with her anyway.

Act 4 Scene 2

Maria gets Feste to dress up as a priest sends him to see Malvolio. Sir Toby watches while Feste tests him with witty jokes and tells him he's mad, even though Malvolio insists he isn't.

Sir Toby realizes he's in Olivia's bad books for fighting with Cesario and gets Feste to go and see Malvolio again, this time as himself. Malvolio asks him for a pen and paper, and a light so that he can see to write a note to Olivia.

Act 4 Scene 3

Sebastian is very confused but he can't believe his luck, meeting a woman like Olivia, who seems to be very keen on him. He wonders what's happened to Antonio, not knowing he's been arrested.

Olivia comes back with a priest. Still thinking Sebastian is is Cesario, she asks him if he will vow before the priest to marry her.

Sebastian agrees immediately and they follow the priest to the chapel.

Act 5 Scene 1

Feste is on his way to see Olivia. He has Malvolio's note with him. Fabian wants to see if it incriminates him, but Feste won't hand it over.

Orsino comes in with Cesario. Orsino is determined to make Olivia see him. He jokes with Feste and pays him to bring her out.

Feste goes. Antonio is dragged in by the police. Orsino knows him and tells them he's a pirate. Cesario tells Orsino that Antonio saved him earlier, although he had not understood what Antonio had meant when he went on about their friendship and the money.

Antonio turns on Cesario, still thinking he is Sebastian. Antonio tells how he saved him from the shipwreck as well as from Sir Toby and Sir Andrew. Everyone is confused when Antonio says he has been with him for three months – Cesario has been with Orsino all that time.

Olivia comes in and ignores Orsino. She wants to know where Cesario has been. Orsino is furious and starts to leave, with Cesario following him.

Olivia asks where Cesario is going. Cesario confesses love for Orsino. Olivia thinks Cesario has betrayed her and asks why her 'husband' is behaving this way.

Orsino is even more furious as *he* thinks Cesario has betrayed *him*.

Olivia calls the priest to remind Cesario of their ceremony in the chapel.

Sir Andrew bursts on stage well and truly beaten up. He tells everybody he's been injured by Cesario. Cesario protests that he hasn't done anything.

Feste helps Sir Toby in. He's sober at last but hurt and calling for a surgeon. Sir Toby and Sir Andrew fall out.

Sebastian arrives and apologizes to Olivia for beating up Sir Toby and Sir Andrew. Everyone is astonished.

Sebastian is amazed to see Cesario. He says he used to have a sister but not a brother.

Cesario/Viola tells Sebastian where she comes from and asks if he is a ghost. They each realize who the other one is. Viola says she can take them to the Captain who saved her. He has her female clothes but is locked up in a prison because of a quarrel with Malvolio.

© Irene Yates

This page may be photocopied for use by the purchasing institution only.

How to Dazzle at Twelfth Night

www.brilliantpublications.co.uk   11

Orsino realizes he loves Viola, not Olivia.

Olivia sends for Malvolio. Feste gives her the note from Malvolio and she realizes he's not mad afterall.

Olivia offers to have Orsino and Viola's wedding at her house, at the same time as her own.

When Malvolio arrives he tells Olivia she has done him wrong. He shows her the love letter but Olivia points out that it isn't her writing, it is Maria's.

Fabian tells all, that he and Sir Toby set up the trick. He says Sir Toby has married Maria as repayment for writing the letter. Fabian says it was all a joke.

Feste starts reminding Malvolio of all that happened. He tells him he was the priest who said Malvolio was mad and that he'd done it to get his own back for Malvolio being rude about him.

Malvolio storms out, promising revenge.

Orsino sends somebody after him. For the time being, Viola must remain as Cesario but soon she will be able to claim her clothes and her real identity. Feste sings the final song about how fooling about can start off being innocent fun but can end disastrously.

Add-on
Which character do you like the most? Why?
Which character do you dislike the most? Why?

Who's who?

Draw lines to match the characters with their descriptions.

Olivia's household

Olivia

Maria

Fabian

Malvolio

Sir Toby Belch

Sir Andrew Aguecheek

Feste

A servant

A gentlewoman who attends Olivia

A friend of Sir Toby

Someone who works for Olivia and sometimes for Duke Orsino as well

A relative of Olivia's, living at her house

A steward, who organizes the house and servants

A wealthy countess

■■■■■■■■■■■■■■■■■■■■■■■■

Orsino's household

Duke Orsino

Valentine

Curio

Feste

An attendant

Someone who works for Duke Orsino and sometimes for Olivia

An attendant

The ruler of Illyria

■■■■■■■■■■■■■■■■■■■■■■■■

The others. Who are they? Could one be a trick?

Viola

Sebastian

Antonio

Cesario

Viola's twin brother

Sebastian's twin sister

A woman disguised as a man

A seafarer who rescues Sebastian

Add-on

Which character do you think is the easiest one to learn about? Why?

Which do you think is the hardest character to learn about? Why?

© Irene Yates

This page may be photocopied for use by the purchasing institution only.

How to Dazzle at Twelfth Night

www.brilliantpublications.co.uk

13

Who's in the play?

Hidden in the grid below are the names of the characters we come across in *Twelfth Night*. Can you find them?

```
F  F  G  X  N  A  I  T  S  A  B  E  S  C  A  V  K  L  R  A
A  I  J  L  U  L  A  W  T  U  N  N  E  J  A  O  N  C  A  S
H  O  S  D  U  O  L  I  V  I  A  I  T  S  A  Q  U  A  T  N
R  B  I  T  A  I  Q  U  S  I  R  T  O  B  Y  B  E  L  C  H
U  T  S  G  E  V  E  A  I  C  A  N  F  K  L  P  C  E  E  G
T  H  I  D  G  R  O  B  M  E  T  E  J  L  O  X  T  H  A  J
S  A  N  D  O  I  W  H  A  C  D  L  M  V  P  S  H  U  S  H
N  L  S  I  R  A  N  D  R  E  W  A  G  U  E  C  H  E  E  K
B  E  H  A  S  D  E  Y  I  J  H  V  A  F  P  I  K  U  C  A
A  N  S  H  I  L  S  H  A  N  T  O  N  I  O  D  R  F  E  E
H  E  X  V  N  I  O  T  H  A  S  H  U  N  O  W  N  I  C  L
C  U  R  I  O  V  R  S  O  I  L  O  V  L  A  M  Q  U  A  M
A  U  M  U  C  R  O  P  E  B  E  T  O  P  B  E  I  A  B  C
T  R  I  O  F  J  H  X  R  A  S  T  U  L  O  I  P  R  A  D
E  G  U  H  R  S  K  A  Q  F  Y  I  V  D  L  K  J  E  O  D
```

These are the names you have to find.

Cesario
Sir Andrew Aguecheek
Orsino
Maria
Malvolio

Curio
Valentine
Feste
Antonio
Fabian

Sebastian
Olivia
Sir Toby Belch
Viola

Add-on

Which two characters are really one?

© Irene Yates

Where do they all belong?

Place the characters in the household to which they belong.

Orsino's household

Olivia's household

The visitors

Watch out! There may be a tricky
one here! Clue: he's not always where
he belongs.

Antonio	**Cesario**	**Curio**	**Duke Orsino**
Fabian	**Feste**	**Malvolio**	**Maria**
Olivia	**Sebastian**	**Sir Toby**	**Sir Andrew**
Valentine	**Viola**	**Guards**	**Sailors**

Factfile – all about Orsino

Read the passage below and fill in the blanks using the words from the word bank.

The Duke Orsino is ruler of _____. He is in love with

_____. He's rich and powerful, but sends _____

to see _____ instead of going himself.

He can't think of anything except being in _____ .

He's in for a big surprise – well, two big surprises.

The first is – he thinks _____ has married _____ .

But the biggest surprise is that _____ is really _____ .

It all ends happily ever after because they get _____ .

Word bank			
Cesario	Cesario	Olivia	Olivia
Viola	love	married	Illyria
Olivia	Cesario		

Add-on

I think Orsino is

because

Factfile – all about Viola

Read the passage below and fill in the blanks using the words from the word bank.

Viola and her brother, _____ , get _____ .

Viola ends up in _____ , thinking Sebastian has _____ .

She dresses up as a _____ and gets a job at the court of Duke

_____ . She calls herself _____ . Unfortunately, she

falls in love with _____ .

The Duke sends _____ to tell _____ that he loves

her. But _____ falls for _____ ! Viola goes with the

flow. She keeps her _____ right up to the end. Viola is

_____ and _____ .

Word bank			
Illyria	secret	Cesario	Cesario
Cesario	Olivia	Olivia	Orsino
Orsino	drowned	boy	cool
Sebastian	shipwrecked	calm	

Add-on

I think Viola is

because

Factfile – all about Sebastian

Read the passage below and fill in the blanks using the words from the word bank.

Sebastian is _____ twin brother. They look exactly _____ .

When _____ pretends to be _____ , she wears

clothes exactly the _____ as her brother's. Sebastian, _____

from the shipwreck by _____ , thinks that his sister has

_____ .

When Sebastian gets to _____ he wants to see the sights.

Everybody thinks Sebastian is _____ . Sir _____ and Sir

_____ attack him and he's happy to _____ back. He's happy

to go along with _____ even though he doesn't think the situation makes

sense. Sebastian is a bit of a _____ .

Word bank

Andrew	madcap
Cesario	Cesario
Illyria	Viola's
Viola	alike
Antonio	fight
Toby	Olivia
same	drowned
rescued	

Add-on

I think Sebastian is

because

Factfile – all about Olivia

Read the passage below and fill in the blanks using the words from the word bank.

Olivia is a beautiful _____ . She lives in the same town as _____

_____ . Her father and brother have died and she has _____

herself away. But when she sees _____ she falls in love with him.

She doesn't know he is really _____ . She is so madly in love that she

can't keep control of her _____ . The trick on _____

works because she can't think straight. She gets engaged to _____

thinking he is _____ .

Olivia is _____ and _____ to begin with but she begins to look really

_____ when she falls in love. She makes a _____ of herself in

front of everyone.

Word bank
locked
Duke Orsino
silly
Sebastian
a girl
sad
lonely
countess
Cesario
fool
Cesario
Malvolio
household

Add-on

I think Olivia is

because

Factfile – all about Malvolio

Read the passage below and fill in the blanks using the words from the word bank.

Malvolio is Olivia's _____ . He is her servant boss, looking after the

household. He tells _____ what to do. He is _____ and

_____ . Nobody likes Malvolio except _____ .

When he upsets _____ , she tricks him by writing a _____

_____ that looks as if it has come from Olivia. Malvolio is so

_____ he already thinks Olivia has feelings for him. Now, he is

convinced. He does all the _____ things the letter tells him to do, thinking

he is proving his _____ for Olivia. She thinks he has gone mad, and gets

_____ _____ to look after him. Now it all gets _____ . Sir Toby

and Maria _____ him up and play more tricks on him. In the end, Malvolio

storms off, promising _____ .

<table>
<tr><td colspan="2">Word bank</td></tr>
<tr><td>bossy</td><td>steward</td></tr>
<tr><td>Maria</td><td>rude</td></tr>
<tr><td>Olivia</td><td>Sir Toby</td></tr>
<tr><td>arrogant</td><td>love letter</td></tr>
<tr><td>revenge</td><td>lock</td></tr>
<tr><td>silly</td><td>everyone</td></tr>
<tr><td>nasty</td><td>love</td></tr>
</table>

Add-on

I think Malvolio is

because

Factfile – all about Sir Toby Belch

Read the passage below and fill in the blanks using the words from the word bank.

Sir Toby is Olivia's _____ . He lives at her house because he is

_____ . He _____ off her. He sponges off his friend Sir

_____ _____ , and makes him think he can get

Olivia to _____ him. Sir Toby thinks Olivia is stupid to be in mourning

and most of the time he is _____ . He'll do anything for a

_____ , though most of his games aren't _____ . He hates

Malvolio and he talks Sir Andrew into the duel with _____ just for a

laugh. It's not such a laugh when he's being beaten up by _____ .

He marries _____ at the end of the play and sobers up a bit.

Word bank	
drunk	funny
marry	uncle
laugh	broke
Sebastian	Andrew
Cesario	sponges
Maria	Aguecheek

Add-on

I think Sir Toby is

because

Factfile – all about
Sir Andrew Aguecheek

Read the passage below and fill in the blanks using the words from the word bank.

Sir Andrew is Sir Toby's 'best _____'. He's not really very _____.

He can't keep up with Sir Toby's _____ and never knows when Sir Toby's

taking the mickey out of him. Sir Toby is really only friends with him because he's

got _____.

Sir Andrew doesn't really stand a chance with _____ but believes Sir

Toby when he keeps saying he'll fix it. He is a _____ but even when

he's being _____ you can't help thinking he might be all right really if it

weren't for _____ _____.

He's really quite a _____ person because all his friends are only using him

and he can't see it.

Word bank

silly	bright
money	coward
sad	friend
Sir Toby	jokes
Olivia	

Add-on

I think Sir Andrew is

because

Factfile – all about Maria

Read the passage below and fill in the blanks using the words from the word bank.

Maria is important because she is the one who plays the trick on

_____ . Maria is Olivia's personal _____ . She looks after

her.

Sir Toby is one of her _____ . She _____ him that Olivia is

getting fed up with him. She also warns _____ that Olivia is annoyed

about him disappearing. Feste can see that Maria and Toby would be a _____

_____.

Maria is really angry when Malvolio tells her off for giving Sir Toby and Sir Andrew

more _____ . She writes a trick _____ _____ to get her

own back.

At the end of the play, Fabian says that Sir Toby has _____ her.

Word bank

maid   Feste
love letter   warns
friends   married
wine   good match
Malvolio

be not afraid
of greatness:
some are born
to be great

Add-on

I think Maria is

because

Factfile – all about Feste

Read the passage below and fill in the blanks using the words from the word bank.

Feste is a professional _____ . It is his job to make jokes and _____ around. He can say anything he likes, even if it _____ people. Most of his jokes are _____ and _____ . Almost everything he says has a _____ meaning. He entertains for _____ and goes to whoever will pay him. He sings sad songs for _____ when he's feeling low, and sad love songs for Sir Toby and Sir Andrew when they are _____ .

Feste hates _____ and pretends to be the _____ to get his revenge on him for saying bad things about him to Olivia.

Word bank	
money	puns
upsets	fool
drunk	wordplay
clown	Orsino
Malvolio	priest
double	

Add-on

I think Feste is

because

Factfile – all about Fabian

Read the passage below and fill in the blanks using the words from the word bank.

Fabian is a servant in _____ household. Like Feste he also

_____ Malvolio. This is because Malvolio got him into _____

once with Olivia, about organizing some _____ . He joins in the

_____ with the others. He also winds up _____ _____ ,

with Sir Toby, to take on a duel with _____ .

Fabian is the one who _____ everything before Malvolio can

investigate who really played the trick. He says he planned it with Sir _____

and it was all meant to be a _____ .

Word bank

bear-baiting	confesses	Olivia's	hates
Sir Andrew	trouble	pranks	joke
	Cesario	Toby	

Factfile – all about Antonio

Read the passage below and fill in the blanks using the words from the word bank.

Antonio is a _____ . He is _____ friend. Antonio

rescues Sebastian from the _____ . Sebastian and Antonio stay

together for three _____ .

Antonio follows Sebastian to _____ . Unfortunately, Antonio once got

involved in a _____ with one of _____ ships. If Orsino comes

across him, Antonio will be captured. He needs to _____ .

When Antonio sees Cesario with Sir Andrew, he thinks it is _____ , so

he rescues him. But the boy hasn't got his money so he thinks he has

_____ it.

At the end of the play we don't know if Antonio will be _____ _____ or

_____ ____ .

Word bank			
Illyria	**battle**	**sea-captain**	**shipwreck**
stolen	**Sebastian's**	**hide**	**Sebastian**
let off	**locked up**	**months**	**Orsino's**

True or false?

Probably the hardest part to learn and remember about this play is that Viola is Cesario, and Cesario is really Viola. If you can remember this, you have cracked it. All the characters in the play think that Viola is Cesario, but it's difficult because all the stage directions refer to Viola.

Read the statements below carefully. Mark True or False in the box. Be careful because some of them are quite tricky!

1. Viola and Cesario are the same person. .... ☐

2. Cesario falls in love with Olivia. .... ☐

3. Viola is Sebastian's twin brother. .... ☐

4. All the characters in the play think that Cesario is a man. .... ☐

5. There is some cross-dressing going on here. .... ☐

6. The play gets more complicated when Sebastian appears. .... ☐

7. Olivia falls in love with Cesario. .... ☐

8. Cesario beats up Sir Andrew Aguecheek. .... ☐

9. The only person who knows the truth about Viola is the Captain of the shipwrecked boat from which they survived. .... ☐

10. Antonio saves Sebastian from Sir Andrew. .... ☐

11. Viola models her 'male' clothes on Sebastian's. .... ☐

12. Olivia marries Cesario. .... ☐

Add-on

Write a brief account of Viola's story in your own words.

A–Z of Twelfth Night

Give answers to the following. You may need to use a dictionary to help you.

A is the person who rescued Sebastian from the shipwreck. _____

B is the surname of Lady Olivia's uncle. _____

C is the title given to the leader of a ship. _____

D is the main man in Illyria . _____

E is the name given to the inn where Antonio stayed in hiding. _____

F is the person who confessed all. _____

G are what Malvolio wears over his stockings. _____

H is the word Olivia uses to describe the relationship of her

loved one to her. _____

I is the setting for the play. _____

J is the position that Feste held. _____

K is another Shakespearian word for the J above. _____

L Is music the food of this? _____

M is a rude and arrogant man. _____

N is the commotion made by Sir Toby and Sir Andrew. _____

O The Lady of the house, in mourning for her brother. _____

P Maria is the mastermind for these _____

Q is for the dilemma occurring. _____

R is for the wet stuff referred to in Feste's closing song

denoting no good lasts for ever. _____

S is what has happened before the play starts. _____

T is the pretend priest who visits Malvolio. _____

U is what the plot does to reveal the truth! _____

V is one of a twin and two in one! _____

W is the word referred to as women's clothes. _____

X is how Malvolio wore his stockings. _____

Y Were they truly this colour? _____

Z is the name given to a clown's assistant on stage. _____

What I want, what I really, really want . . .

Each of the following characters wants something different. Some of their desires change as the play progresses. **Choose what you think their main aim is, and write a couple of sentences to describe what they really, really want.**

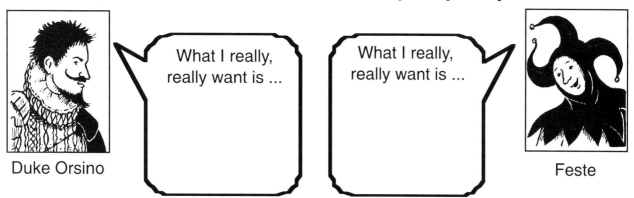

Duke Orsino — What I really, really want is ...

What I really, really want is ... — Feste

Viola — What I really, really want is ...

What I really, really want is ... — Sir Toby

Antonio — What I really, really want is ...

What I really, really want is ... — Olivia

Direct your own play

Imagine you are going to produce *Twelfth Night*. You need to give your actors and actresses some direction on the characters they are playing. You need to tell them how you want them to play their parts. **Write *notes* in the boxes below to help you decide what to say to each actor or actress.**

Olivia	Viola/Cesario	Sir Toby Belch

Duke Orsino	Maria	Feste

Sir Andrew Aguecheek	Sebastian	Malvolio

Elizabethan England

Twelfth Night is full of language which gives us sights, sounds and customs of Shakespearian England. **Look at the examples below and put them into the box where you think they belong.**

buttery-bar	caper	woodcock	points
bum-baily	parish top	whipstock	toss-pots
branched velvet gown	parson	jig	hounds
cherry-pit	coziers	yellow stockings	cold scent
sack	pickled herring	back trick	coistrill
gaskins	fox	cantons	bear-baiting
the Elephant	cross-gartered	catch	aleshouse
St Bennet	Dick Surgeon		

Hunting and sports	Food and drink	Occupations

Songs and dances	Clothes	Places and customs

Tricky language

Shakespeare's language is quite tricky until you get the hang of it. It's better to read it out loud than in your head – after all, it was written as a play!

Basically, the script is written in **poetry** and **prose**. Prose is any kind of language that isn't poetry. You can recognize the **poetry**: each line begins with a capital letter, even if it's in the middle of a sentence. The poetry always has ten or eleven syllables in each line. Sometimes the last syllable of the line rhymes with the end of the next line:

If music be the food of love, play on,
1   2   3   4   5   6   7   8   9   10

Act 1, Sc 1
line 1

I'll follow this good man, and go with you, **And having sworn truth, ever will be true.**

Act 4, Sc 3
lines 31–2

Sometimes the poetry doesn't rhyme. This is called **blank verse**.

Your lord does know my mind. I cannot love him. **Yet I suppose him virtuous, know him noble,**

Act 1, Sc 5,
lines 241–2

Prose is anything that isn't poetry. It has long sentences!

What a plague means my niece to take **the death of her brother thus? I am sure care's an** **enemy to life.**

Act 1, Sc 3
lines 1–3

Look up these lines. Say whether they are:
- A. poetry
- B. blank verse, or
- C. prose.

1. Act 1, Sc 4, lines 14–19   Therefore, good youth ...

2. Act 1, Sc 5, lines 297–8   Fate, show thy force ...

3. Act 2, Sc 5, lines 193– 9   If you will then see ...

4. Act 3, Sc 4, lines 152–4   'Fare thee well ...'

5. Act 5, Sc 1, lines 138–9   Husband? ...

Old and new

There are lots of small words in the play that make the language look trickier than it really is. We now use other words instead. **Draw a line to link the old words with the new.**

thou	I ask you
thee	has
dost	are
wilt	to here
thy	you
art	do
hast	will
hither	you
hath	have
prithee	your

Find examples of five of these words and write references for the lines they are in.

For example,

| How now, art thou mad? | Act 5, Sc 1, line 281 |

1. _____

2. _____

3. _____

4. _____

5. _____

Looking at imagery 1

Twelfth Night is full of **imagery**. Images are figures of speech used to make you conjure up pictures in your mind. They help you to see what Shakespeare is trying to describe. There are three kinds of image to watch out for: *metaphor, simile* and *personification*.

Metaphor

A metaphor is when Shakespeare says one thing but means something else. For example, Feste says that 'time is a **whirligig**'. A whirligig is a spinning top. So by making a reference in this manner, he means that what goes around, comes around.

And thus the whirligig of time brings in his revenges.	Act 5, Sc 1, lines 360–1

Find eight examples of *metaphor* within the play. Write down your answers on the spider diagram below. Don't forget to include where they came from. One is done for you.

Maria:
Will you hoist sail, Sir? Here lies your way.
(Act 1, Sc 5, line 203)

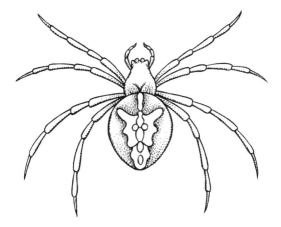

Help: Metaphors are hard work until you suddenly 'get' them. Think of the easy ones you know first, like *Pick your feet up!* or *Keep your eye on the ball!* You wouldn't interpret these sayings literally, would you?

Looking at imagery 2

Twelfth Night is full of **imagery**. Images are figures of speech used to make you conjure up pictures in your mind. They help you to see what Shakespeare is trying to describe. There are three kinds of image to watch out for: *simile*, *metaphor* and *personification*.

Simile

A simile is when Shakespeare describes one thing as being like something else.

Similies usually use the words 'as' or 'like' so they are more easily recognized than metaphors. They compare things. For example, Orsino compares his love for Olivia with the size and tumult of the sea.

> But mine is all as hungry as the sea,
> And can digest as much.

Act 2, Sc 4, lines 96–7

Find eight examples of *simile* within the play. Write down your answers on the spider diagram below. Don't forget to include where they come from. One is done for you.

Fabian:
... where you will hang like an icicle on a Dutchman's beard
(Act 3, Sc 2, lines 26–27)

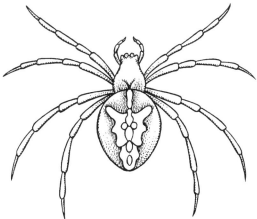

Help: Similes are easy to spot. Think of ones you know first, such as *as green as grass* or *it's as black as night*.

Looking at imagery 3

Twelfth Night is full of **imagery**. Images are figures of speech used to make you conjure up pictures in your mind. They help you to see what Shakespeare is trying to describe. There are three kinds of image to watch out for: *personification, simile* and *metaphor*.

Personification

Personification means describing something as if it were a person and not a thing. It is a special kind of metaphor. For example, Olivia makes the clock sound as if it were a person. She says it is criticising her for wasting time.

| The clock upbraids me with the waste of time. | Act 3, Sc 1, line 126 |

Personification can be much harder to spot than similes, and sometimes, if you're not careful, it gets muddled up with other metaphors.

While you are reading the play, write down any examples of personification that you can find.

Help: Imagery makes you use your imagination.

Add-on

Write an example of personification in modern language.

Text messaging

If Elizabethans had had mobile phones, none of this could have happened! **Write some text messages that might have saved them all the trouble!**

1. Viola to Sebastian when she is rescued by the Captain.

2. Duke Orsino to Olivia at the beginning of the play.

3. Olivia to Cesario when 'he' goes back to the Duke.

4. Malvolio to the two knights when they're having their drunken party.

5. Fabian to Malvolio after Maria has tricked him.

6. Malvolio to Olivia when he's locked up.

7. Antonio to Sebastian when he's taken away by the police.

8. Viola to Orsino when she understands what's happened.

9. Feste to all the characters at the end of the play.

Who said what to whom?

Fill in the names of the characters who said the lines below. If you can, write in the references for the text.

1. You mistake, Knight. 'Accost' is front her, board her,
   woo her, assail her.   _____

2. It alone concerns your ear ... I hold the olive in my
   hand: my words are full of peace, as matter   _____

3. If music be the food of love, play on   _____

4. I am all the daughters of my father's house,
   And all the brothers too: and yet I know not.   _____

5. ... like a cloistress, she will veiled walk   _____

6. ... one would think his mother's milk were
   scarce out of him.   _____

7. ... yet, a barful strife!
   whoe'er I woo, myself would be his wife?   _____

8. Away before me to sweet beds of flowers!
   Love – thoughts lie rich when canopied with bowers. _____

9. How now?
   Even so quickly may one catch this plague?   _____

10. ... he does smile his face into more lines than is in the
    new map with the augmentation of the Indies   _____

Choose from:

Maria to Sir Toby and Fabian

Orsino to Valentine	Viola to Orsino	Viola to herself
Valentine to Orsino	Malvolio to Olivia	Orsino to Curio
Viola to Olivia	Olivia to herself	Sir Toby to Sir Andrew

The key words

Two key words describe *Twelfth Night*. **Complete the following puzzle and you will find out what they are.**

1. Where does the play take place?
2. What kind of play is it?
3. Who is really the main character?
4. What event happened before the play begins?
5. How is Olivia feeling at the beginning of the play?
6. Who is Sir Toby's friend?
7. How does Malvolio treat people?
8. Who is responsible for the trick played on Malvolio?
9. Who is Viola disguised as?
10. Most of Feste's jokes are based on what?
11. Who does Viola fall in love with?
12. What does Maria write?
13. Whose entrance heralds a big surprise?
14. Who closes the play?

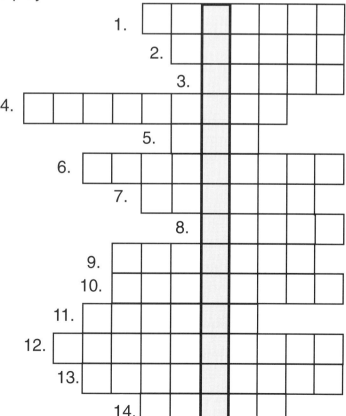

What's in a play?

A play is meant to be acted out in front of people, not read inside your head.
Answer the following questions to complete the puzzle and to find out how much you can remember.

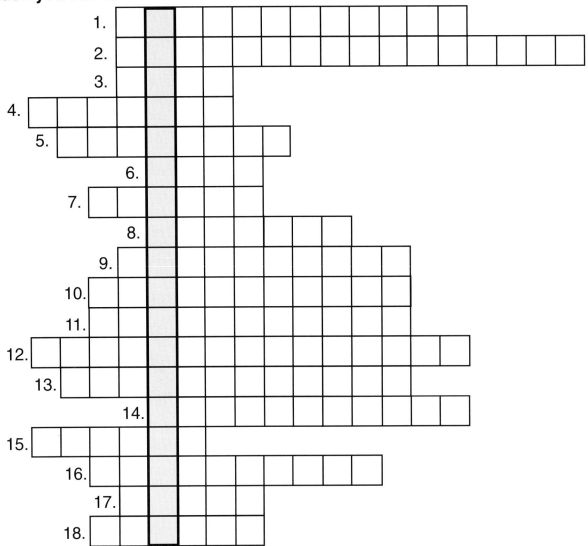

1. This play (7,5)
2. It's a case of ... , – a disguise that caused a lot of confusion. (8,8)
3. The name given to the main story line. (4)
4. The name for secondary story line. (7)
5. A play needs this to watch it! (8)
6. The play is split into five of these. (4)
7. A funny kind of play. (6)
8. Where the drama takes place. (4)
9. Actors play these. (10)

10. Serious, theatrical. (8)
11. Illyria is a land of this. (11)
12. These tell the actors what to do – type of 'cue card'. (5,10)
13. A banquet for clowns? – held on 6th January. (5,2,5)
14. What an actor tries to give his best of. (11)
15. Some of the text does this. (6)
16. And some of the text is this. (5,5)
17. Two-thirds of the text is this. (5)
18. Each act is split into these. (6)

Soap opera – the Illyrians

Suppose you are going to produce a new soap opera on TV, called *The Illyrians*.
Write a quick sketch of the main characters and your first six episodes.
Choose six events from the play that capture your imagination. Try to see *The Illyrians* like *Eastenders* or *Coronation Street*.

Main characters

Episodes

Add-on

How do you think the soap will continue?

Write your own glossary
Key vocabulary from Act 1, Scenes 1–3

Look at these words. The meanings are given below, but which is which? Write the words in alphabetical order. Then write the meaning next to each one. The first one is done for you as an example.

practice (Scene 2, line 13)

cloistress (Scene 1, line 28)

abjured (Scene 2, line 40)

fancy (Scene 1, line 14)

canary (Scene 3, line 76)

distaff (Scene 3, line 99)

accost (Scene 3, line 45)

kickshawes (Scene 3, line 107)

surfeiting (Scene 1, line 2)

coranto (Scene 3, line 119)

abjured = sworn not to be

_____

_____

_____

_____

_____

_____

_____

_____

_____

_____

Help: If you look the words up in the text, you will have the context to help you.

Choose from: sworn not to be   a type of dance   nun

silly things   spindle   skill   pay a compliment

love   too much   sweet wine from Canary Islands

Add-on

Add more words to your glossary.

Write your own glossary
Key vocabulary from Act 1, Scene 5

Look at these words. The meanings are given below, but which is which? Write the words in alphabetical order. Then write the meaning next to each one. The first one is done for you as an example.

zanies (Scene 5, line 87)

inventoried (Scene 5, line 230)

points (Scene 5, line 21)

syllogism (Scene 5, line 46)

blazon (Scene 5, line 280)

heresy (Scene 5, line 216)

blent (Scene 5, line 226)

nonpareil (Scene 5, line 243)

swabber (Scene 5, line 194)

catechize (Scene 5, line 58)

blazon = coats of arms

_____

_____

_____

_____

_____

_____

_____

_____

_____

_____

Help: If you look the words up in the text, you will have the context to help you.

Choose from: deck scrubber   ask questions   coat of arms

blended   lies   listed   clown's assistant

formula   laces to hold up gaskins   the most beautiful of all

Add-on

Add more words to your glossary.

Write your own glossary
Key vocabulary from Act 2, Scene 5

Look at these words and phrases. The meanings are given below, but which is which? Write the words and phrases in alphabetical order. Then write the meaning next to each one. The first one is done for you as an example.

jets (line 29)

services (line 154)

branched (line 44)

fustian (line 103)

probation (line 123)

aqua vitae (line 191)

Tartar (line 199)

staniel checks (line 108)

gin (line 79)

no consonancy (line 191)

aqua vitae = alcoholic spirit

_____

_____

_____

_____

_____

_____

_____

_____

_____

Help: If you look the words up in the text, you will have the context to help you.

Choose from:
roles	alcoholic spirit	kestrel darts
trap	worthless	scrutiny	hell
embroidered	struts about	it doesn't make sense

Add–on

Add more words to your glossary.

Write your own glossary
Key vocabulary from Act 3, Scene 1

Look at these words and phrases. The meanings are given below, but which is which? Write the words and phrases in alphabetical order. Then write the meaning next to each one. The first one is done for you as an example.

feigning (line 95)

odours (line 81)

commodity (line 41)

out of my welkin (line 57)

list (line 73)

maugre (line 148)

upbraids (line 126)

I am loath (line 21)

tabor (stage directions)

gait (line 77)

commodity = hand-out

_____

_____

_____

_____

_____

_____

_____

_____

_____

_____

Help: If you look the words up in the text, you will have the context to help you.

Choose from:

Choose from:	small drum	I don't want to	steps
none of my business	despite	sweet fragrances	hand-out
destination	pretending	tells me off	

Add-on

Add more words to your glossary.

Write your own glossary
Key vocabulary from Act 3, Scene 4

Look at these words and phrases. The meanings are given below, but which is which? Write the words and phrases in alphabetical order. Then write the meaning next to each one. The first one is done for you as an example.

virago (line 209)

the Sophy (line 279)

horribly conceited (line 270)

necessity (line 309)

miscarry (line 59)

cockatrices (line 178)

bum-baily (line 161)

yare (line 206)

daws (line 33)

mortal arbitrement (line 24)

bum-baily = bailiff

_____

_____

_____

_____

_____

_____

_____

_____

_____

Help: If you look the words up in the text, you will have the context to help you.

Choose from: monstrous snakes that can kill with a stare   bailiff

female warrior   come to any harm   terrified   tricky situation

quick   fight to the death   jackdaws   the ruler of Persia

Add–on

Add more words to your glossary.

Write your own glossary
Key vocabulary from Act 5, Scene 1

Look at these words and phrases. The meanings are given below, but which is which? Write the words and phrases in alphabetical order. Then write the meaning next to each one. The first one is done for you as an example.

record (line 235)   on base and ground enough (line 68)

savours nobly (line 114)   habits (line 386)

dressed (line 204)   maiden weeds (line 254)

at this throw (line 36)   sot (line 188)

recommended to his use (line 85)   but that's all one (line 257)

at this throw = this time around

_____

_____

_____

_____

_____

_____

_____

_____

_____

_____

Help: If you look the words up in the text, you will have the context to help you.

Choose from:	bandaged	feels right	this time around
memory	lent him	with good reason	old drunk
Who cares?	girl's clothes	clothes	

Add-on

Add more words to your glossary.

Answers

Who's in the play? – page 14

```
F F G X N A I T S A B E S C A V K L R A
A I J L U L A W T U N N E J A O N C A S
H O S D U O L I V I A I T S A Q U A T N
R B I T A I Q U S I R T O B Y B E L C H
U T S G E V E A I C A N F K L P C E E G
T H I D G R O B M E T E J L O X T H A J
S A N D O I W H A C D L M V P S H U S H
N L S R A N D R E W A G U E C H E E K
B E H A S D E Y I J H V A F P I K U C A
A N H I L S H A N T O N I O D R F E E
H E X V N I O T H A S H U N O W N I C L
C U R I O V R S O I L O V L A M Q U A M
A U M U C R O P E B E T O P B E I A B C
T R I O F J H X R A S T U L O I P R A D
E G U H R S K A Q F Y I V D L K J E O D
```

Where do they all belong? – page 15

Olivia's household: Olivia, Sir Toby, Maria, Fabian, Malvolio, Feste
Orsino's household: Duke Orsino, Valentine, Curio, Cesario, Feste, Guards
The visitors: Sir Andrew, Viola, Antonio, Sebastian, Sailors.

Factfile – all about Orsino – page 16
Illyria, Olivia, Cesario, Olivia, love, Cesario, Olivia, Cesario, Viola, married

Factfile – all about Viola – page 17
Sebastian, shipwrecked, Illyria, drowned, boy, Orsino, Cesario, Orsino, Cesario, Olivia, Olivia, Cesario, secret, cool, calm

Factfile – all about Sebastian – page 18
Viola's, alike, Viola, Cesario, same, rescued, Antonio, drowned, Illyria, Cesario, Toby, Andrew, fight, Olivia, madcap

Factfile – all about Olivia – page 19
countess, Duke Orsino, locked, Cesario, a girl, household, Malvolio, Sebastian, Cesario, sad, lonely, silly, fool

Factfile – all about Malvolio – page 20
steward, everyone, rude, bossy, Olivia, Maria, love letter, arrogant, silly, love, Sir Toby, nasty, lock, revenge

Factfile – all about Sir Toby Belch – page 21
uncle, broke, sponges, Andrew, Aguecheek, marry, drunk, laugh, funny, Cesario, Sebastian, Maria

Factfile – all about Sir Andrew Aguecheek – page 22
friend, bright, jokes, money, Olivia, coward, silly, Sir Toby, sad

Factfile – all about Maria – page 23
Malvolio, maid, friends, warns, Feste, good match, wine, love letter, married

Factfile – all about Feste – page 24
fool, clown, upsets, puns, wordplay, double, money, Orsino, drunk, Malvolio, priest

Factfile – all about Fabian – page 25
Olivia's, hates, trouble, bear-baiting, pranks, Sir Andrew, Cesario, confesses, Toby, joke

Factfile – all about Antonio – page 26
sea-captain, Sebastian's, shipwreck, months, Illyria, battle, Orsino's, hide, Sebastian, stolen, let off, locked up.

True or false? – page 27
1. True, 2. False, 3. False, 4. True, 5. True, 6. True, 7. True, 8. False, 9. True, 10. False, 11. True, 12. False

A–Z of Twelfth Night – page 28
A = Antonio, B = Belch, C = Captain, D = Duke, E = Elephant, F = Fabian, G = garters, H = husband, I = Illyria, J = jester, K = knave, L = love, M = Malvolio, N = noise, O = Olivia, P = pranks, Q = quandary, R = rain, S = shipwreck, T = Topas, U = unfolds, V = Viola, W = weeds, X = X-gartered, Y = yellow, Z = zanies

Elizabethan England – page 31
Hunting and sports: bear-baiting, cold scent, fox, hounds, whipstock, woodcock
Food and drink: aleshouse, buttery-bar, pickled herring, sack, toss-pots
Songs and dances: back trick, cantons, caper, catch, jig
Occupations: bum-baily, coistrill, coziers, Dick Surgeon, parson
Places and customs: cherry-pit, the Elephant, parish top, St Bennet
Clothes: branched velvet gown, cross-gartered, gaskins, points, yellow stockings

Tricky language – page 32
1. Blank verse, 2. Poetry, 3. Prose, 4. Prose, 5. Poetry

Old and new – page 33
thou = you, thee = you, dost = do, wilt = will, thy = your, art = are, hast = have, hither = to here, hath = has, prithee = I ask you